Name: _____

Form: _____

AF172853

Settlement

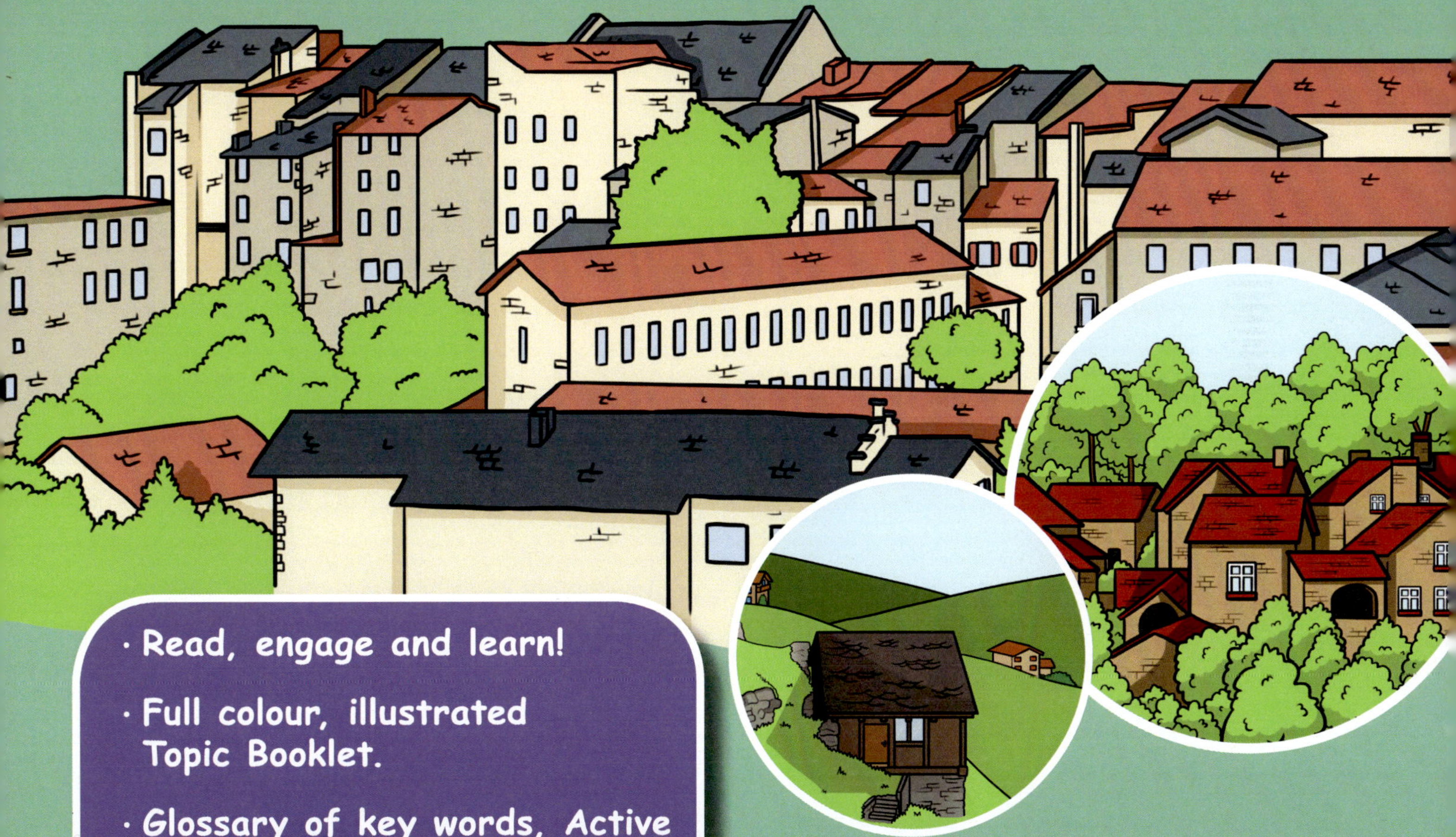

- **Read, engage and learn!**
- **Full colour, illustrated Topic Booklet.**
- **Glossary of key words, Active Learning Game & Flashcards.**
- **Ideal for ISEB 13+ Common Entrance and KS3 pupils.**

Endorsed by:

ISEB Independent Schools Examinations Board

This Oaka™ Books Write Your Own Notes Booklet goes hand in hand with the Active Learning Pack on this topic. The pack includes a Topic Booklet, an Active Learning Game and Question & Answer Flashcards.

Fresh Focus on Learning

Oaka™ BOOKS

Settlement Glossary

Administrative (ad-mini-strah-tiv):
....
....

Brownfield Site: ....
....
....

Central Business District:
....
....
....
....

Commercial: ....
....
....

Green Field Site: ....
....
....

Green Belts: ....
....
....

Industrial: ....
....
....
....

Megacity: ....
....
....

Population: ....
....
....

Residential: ....
....
....

Rural: ....
....

Services: ....
....
....

Settlement: ....
....
....

Site: ....
....
....

Situation: ....
....
....
....

Tourism: ....
....
....
....

Urban: ....
....

Urban Sprawl: ....
....
....

Fill in the blanks using these words to help you...

site   vary   settlement   flood   start   dwelling   flat   small
chosen   temporary   building   different   permanent

1 What is a Settlement?

- A .... is where people live.

- It is any form of ....: from 1 small house to a megacity (millions of people in a city).

2 Settlement Sizes

- Settlements can .... in size, from very .... to very large!

- They can be .... (fixed) or .... (only there for a short time).

3 ....

- Where settlements ...., it is called a site.

- In earlier times, different sites were .... for .... reasons.

- These reasons included...

4 1. ...., Dry Land

- This makes .... easier and safer, and does not ....

5 2. Local ....

- To build .... with and to use as fuel (such as .... and ....).

6 3. .... **Supply**

- Used for drinking, ..., washing, ..., etc.

7 4. Good .... Land

- To grow .... on.

8 5. ....

- To protect from bad .... (such as near a ....).

9   6. ....

- To .... from ....
(such as near a hill top or a
..................................).

10   7. Transport

- Bridging points where ....
routes (over land and ....)
converge assisting .... and
commerce.

11   Situation

- .... is where the
settlement is in .... to
other settlements and features.
- Is it near a forest? Or maybe a
larger town.

12   Growing ....

- If a settlement had lots of
good site .... and a good
situation, then it could ....!
- Many big cities in the UK have
.... because they have
.... site factors and situation.

Fill in the blanks using these words to help you...

functions   town   facilities   100   hamlet   more
village   hierarchy   city   1,000   mega city   primary
pub   population   size   homes

13   Hierarchy

- Settlements can be ranked in order.
- This is called a ....
- Order is decided by ...., ... and services (range and number).

Fewer but more important and bigger

.... settlements

14   Hamlet

- A hamlet has less than .... people dwelling there.
- It has a very small group of ....
- It has few, or no shops or ....
- They do not have a church.

15   Village

- Villages have 100 to .... people.
- They have more ...., such as a church, a shop and a post-office.
- They may even have a .... school, a doctor's practice and a ....

Fill in the blanks using these words to help you...

shopping   cathedral   range   university
100,000   small   wide   population   living   museums
university   shops   specialised   1,000   bank

16   Town

- Towns have a .... of .... to 100,000 people.
- They have a .... of functions.

- These include many ...., schools, train stations, a ...., dentist and a .... hospital.

17   City

- Cities have more than .... people .... there.
- They have a very .... range of functions as well as .... functions.

- These include a ...., sports stadiums, large hospitals, large .... centres, a cathedral and ....

Did you know?
In the past, a city always had a
.... or a ....
Now the Queen decides
which places are cities!

Fill in the blanks using these words to help you...

distance   functions   village   size   megacity   living   hamlets

town   services   travel   bigger   million   three   town

18 ....

- A megacity has more than 10 .... people .... there.
- It has the same .... as a city, but it's much bigger!

19   Remember!

- What may be a .... in one part of the world, could be thought of as a .... in another!

....   Village

20   Is it a city, a town or a village?

- It is not easy as you think! .... things need to be thought about:

Number and range of .... (and how far people may .... to use the services).

Population ....

.... between the settlement and others (many .... may be close together, but towns will have a .... distance between them).

21   Linear

- Settlements develop in a ....

Linear (in a ....):
- along a ...., valley or ....
- often on a .... road between two ....

22   Dispersed

Dispersed (.................. out):

- ....
- farms and houses usually in areas with .... relief.

23   Nucleated

Nucleated (from the word ...., a .... or central point):
- often .... around a water supply/river ...., or at a crossroad.
- also may have been .... around a .... or market place.

Fill in the blanks using these words to help you...

services   restrict   further   tourism   grid   residential
sprawl   purposes   green   transport   commercial   control
industrial   planning   improved   administrative   added   new

24   Planned

Planned:

· Towns which are planned on a square or .... pattern.

· These tend to be .... settlements.

25   Urban Sprawl

· As transport .... in the 1920s, people could live .... from work.

· Urban .... developed and more linear settlements grew along new .... links.

Central Business District

Housing

26   Green Belts

· .... Belts were begun to .... urban sprawl.

· They .... building in rural areas, where it is very difficult to get .... permission.

Green Belt

27   Settlement Functions

The functions of a settlement are its ....

The functions can be split into 6 main groups:

· ....
· ....
· ....
· ....
· ....
· ....

A settlement may start with one function, but some may be ....

Fill in the blanks using these words to help you...

inner   residential   support   outside   detached   commute
dormitory   commercial   extra   terraced   housing   dormitory
cities   shopping   cinemas   overcrowded   towns   retirement

28   ....

- This includes shops in small villages, to large .... centres in .... and ....
- These shopping centres may also include sports and ....

29   **Residential**

- All settlements have housing (................................... function).
- But some are built to provide .... housing because a city may be ....

- These can be called .... settlements and the people .... to work.

30   **Residential**

- .... settlements are found .... the main settlement.
- This consists of ...., semi-detached and .... for people to live in.

- There are also .... villages which offer extra .... for older people.

| Central Business District | .... City (terraced housing) | Inner suburbs (semi-detached) | Outer suburbs (detached) | Green Belt |

Fill in the blanks using these words to help you...

lower   increases   manufacture   settlements
industrial   number   factories   government   people
public   land   smaller   schools   many   factory

31 Administrative

- Local .... has offices and runs .... services.
- These are usually found in larger ....

32 Services

- As the size of a settlement ...., so does the range and .... of services.
- These include doctors' surgeries, ... and hospitals.

33 ....

- Companies which .... (make) products, put their .... in a settlement.
- Big cities often have .... industries because they need .... to work in the ....
- Some industries may locate near .... settlements.
- This is because the price of .... may be ....

34   Tourism

- Many .... have a .... function.
- Big .... have many ...., such as ...., art galleries and ....

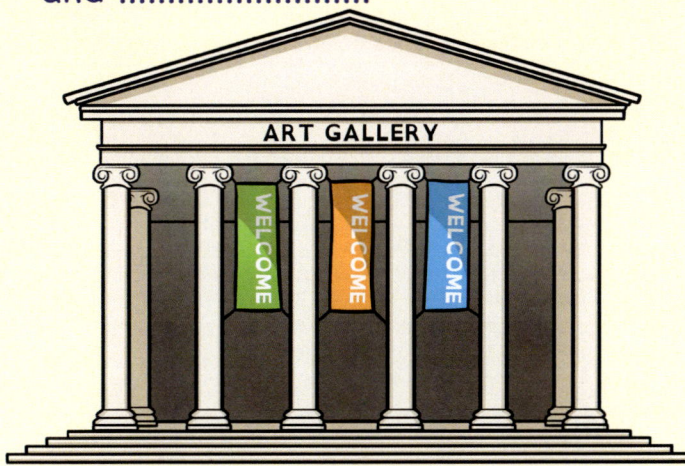

35   Tourism

- Many .... villages are pretty and ....
- .... towns .... many people for .... and holidays.

36 ....

- Villages or small .... which are near a city, may grow ....
- This is because people can .... (called ...., pronounced sub-erb-an-i-zay-shon).

37 Rural Villages

- Many .... villages lose .... people, because there are no ....
- New industries creates .... and people .... to that area.

> I'm moving away from this village to a new area with jobs!

38 Flat Land

- Places that are .... (easy to get to) and have .... land, means that people will build there.

> This place is perfect to build on!

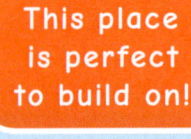

39 Settlements Not Growing

- If there is no .... from other settlements or few site ...., a settlement may not ....

40   The Threshold

- The smallest .... of people needed to .... shops and services is called the ....

- For example, a village probably needs .... people who live in or near it, to have one .... This is a threshold of ....

Small threshold

- A large ...., such as Marks and Spencer, needs a bigger town with a .... threshold to support it (probably 100,000 people!).

M&S

Large threshold

41   The Catchment Area

- Shops also have a ....: it depends on the .... people will travel to reach it.

- The .... area is where the customers ....

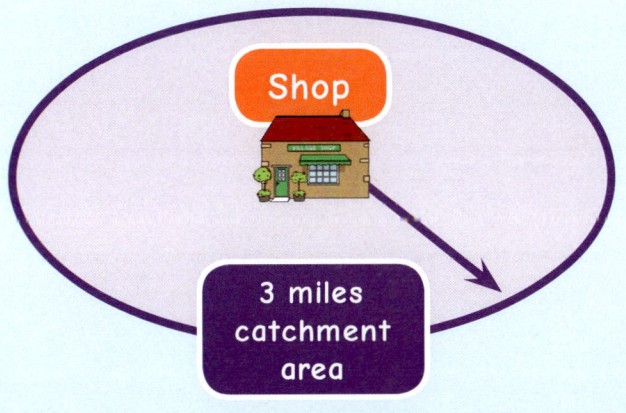

Shop

3 miles catchment area

42   Low .... Service

- People don't travel far to get .... goods, such as bread and milk.

- .... shops sell .... goods, where it has a small range and is called a .... order service.

VILLAGE SHOP

Fill in the blanks using these words to help you...

low   comparison   high order   public   goods
range   expensive   city   travel   village
threshold   buying   large   national   check

43 Comparison ....

- For .... items, such as furniture and computers, people .... prices before ....
- People compare prices, so these are called .... goods.

£150

£360

44 High Order Service

- People will .... further to get their sofa or computer.
- So these shops provide a .... service and have a .... range.

SHOP ONLINE
FREE UK DELIVERY

OakaBook Pro

.... catchment area

45 Public Services

- .... services (like libraries, hospitals and schools) also have a ....
- You will find a hospital in a .... as it has a high .... and high range.

- You will find a primary school in a .... with a .... threshold and a low range.

Welcome to St. Michael's Hospital

HOSPITAL

Primary School

High threshold and high range

Low threshold and low range

Fill in the blanks using these words to help you...

30   27   reused   Queen Elizabeth Park   shops
health   2,818   East Village

46   Olympic Athletes Village

- The 2012 London Olympic Athletes Village has been .... to become a housing development called ....

- It has .... houses.
- They are a mix of private, affordable rental and shared ownership.

47   Where is it?

- It is located within the ...... acres of the .... in London.

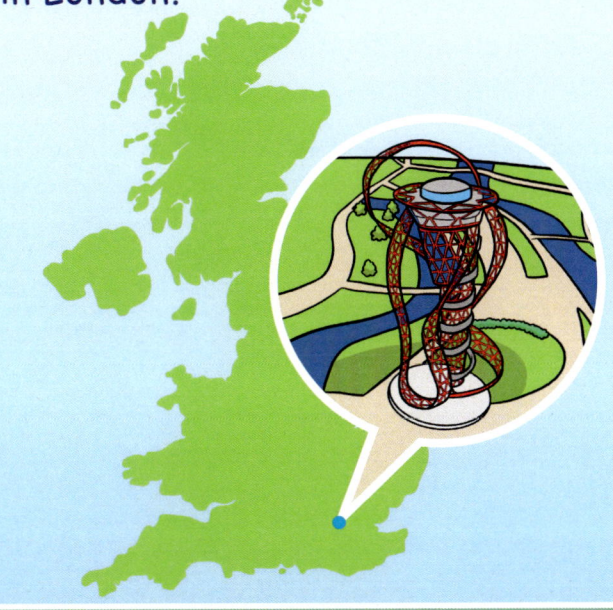

48   Facilities in East Village

- It has .... independent .... and cafes, as well as .... facilities.

30 independent shops and cafes

49 School ....

- There is a .... for 3 to 18 year olds.
- There are also .... for children.

50 Easy To Get To

- London, as well as major .... and shopping centres, are easily ....

51 Construction Stopped!

- In **May 2011**, construction was .... while a rare Black Redstart was ....

Black Redstart

52 Sustainable ....

- The development in this area is built to be ....
- This means it is .... life without .... it for people in years to come.

Sustainable Development

- It does this in a number of ways...

53   Urbanisation

- Many people are moving to .... areas (towns and ....).
- This is happening .... in poorer countries.
- In richer countries, most of the .... already .... in urban areas!

54   Poorer Countries

- .... people in poorer countries live in urban areas.
- So today, this means that .... urbanisation is happening in .... countries.

55   Urbanisation is...

- ...the .... of the number of people living in urban areas.
- It is happening all over the world!
- More than .... of the world's population live in urban areas.
- This increases ....

56   ....-Urban Migration

- Urbanisation is usually caused by ....-Urban ....
- This is the .... of people from the countryside to towns and cities.

57   Urbanisation in Poorer Countries

The reasons for moving are .... in richer and poorer countries.

People in poorer countries .... because:

- Of a .... in services in rural areas (water, ..., power).
- If .... fail, farmers may be forced to move to the .... to feed their families.

I need to earn more .... for my family!

58   Standard of ....

- People believe that the standard of .... is .... in towns and ....
- But this isn't always the case!
- However, there are usually more .... in urban areas than .... areas.

Fill in the blanks using these words to help you...

slums   factories   illegally   squatter   overcrowding
urban   problem   afford   jobs   richer   migrated
shanty   redevelopment   developed   badly

59   Urbanisation in .... Countries

People in .... countries move because:

- In the past, new .... were built in .... areas which created ....
- Today, there is a lot of .... in cities which makes them more attractive.

60   Squatter Settlements

- In poorer countries, ... settlements are a BIG .... (also called .... and .... towns).

61   Problems of Slums

They are:

- Built ....
- Built ....
- There is ....
- Built by people who have .... to the city but can't .... proper housing.

I can't afford proper housing...

 **62** Examples are...

- .... in Brazil.

- .... in India.

63 They can be improved by:

.... schemes:
- The government and people .... together.

64 They can be improved by:

.... and ....:
- People pay a small rent for a site and can borrow .... to build/........................ their house.
- The rent pays for ....

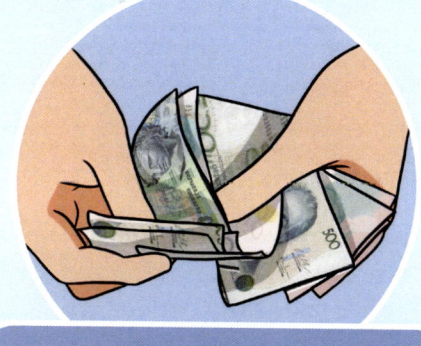

Small .... money

65 They can be improved by:

.... Authority Schemes:
- Funded by the ....
- Offers .... to improve .... housing built by residents.

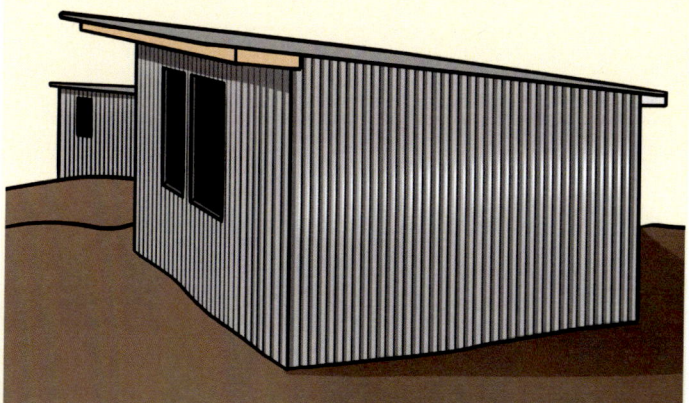

About Oaka Books

Children learn best when they are engaged...

Our aim is to help children enjoy learning by making it fun! That way they will succeed.

This Topic Pack is based on the National Curriculum guidelines for KS3 and ISEB 13+ Common Entrance.

The design and layout of our books follow guidelines from the British Dyslexia Association.

ISBN 978-1-911189-73-2

CE/KS3 Ge-

Settlement

Write Your Own Notes Booklet

Three Easy Steps

Read: the easy to follow bullet point Topic Booklet.

Engage: Play the Active Learning Game.

Learn: When you understand the topic, test yourself using the Write Your Own Notes Book. You can use the Topic Booklet to help if you get stuck.

One (short) Topic at a time:

For some students, a big book is a big turn off. That's why we focus on one topic at a time. Short and to the point.

Reading Age

This booklet is suitable for children with a reading age of 10 years 6 months.

Topic Packs for KS1, KS2 & KS3 Include:

History
Geography
Science
French
Maths

Please visit www.oakabooks.co.uk for more information about forthcoming titles.

© Copyright 2016 Oaka Books. All rights reserved.
Written by Kate Doehren, MA Ed, B.Ed Hons, RSA Dip, Sp LD/Dyslexia - Head of Learning Support, Hurstpierpoint College.
Illustrations by Adora Holcroft.

First paperback edition printed 2015 in the United Kingdom.
A catalogue record for this book is available from the British Library.

ISBN 978-1-911189-19-0
No part of this book shall be reproduced or transmitted in any form or by any means, electronic or mechanical, including photocopying, recording or by any information retrieval system without written permission of the copyright owner or a licence permitting restricted copying issued by the Copyright Licensing Agency Ltd, Saffron House, 6-10 Kirby Street, London EC1N 8TS Tel: 020 7400 3100   Fax: 020 7400 3101   Email: cla@cla.co.uk   Web: www.cla.co.uk

Designed, set and published by Oaka™ Books.

To order other titles from Oaka™ Books, please email info@oakabooks.co.uk or visit www.oakabooks.co.uk, or phone: +44 (023) 92 388 519.

Acknowledgements
Our huge thanks go to the many teachers who have been involved in the development of this series of learning guides. Special thanks to Joy Gardiner, for producing hundreds of illustrations, to Kate Doehren, for her enthusiasm and invaluable assistance to my wonderful daughter Sophie, for being the inspiration for the books and, of course, to Charlie, for believing in them.